"Life's ... even more like that!"

Your guide to the Lebanese

Written by: Peter Grimsditch
& Michael Karam

Illustrated by: Maya Fidawi

Introduced by: Pierre Sadek

Edited by: Faerlie Wilson

Designed by: Reem Abou Chacra

3

Intro by Pierre Sadek

* With all modesty, I am the world...
... and the world is me!

For the few of you who don't know, PIERRE SADEK is Lebanon's most respected political cartoonist. His acerbic sketches in An-Nahar newspaper and Future
Television have ensured that satire is alive and well in Lebanese daily life.

بكل تواضع ..
أنا كل العالم
وكل العالم أنا ؟! *

About us

British-born PETER GRIMSDITCH has been a professional journalist all his life at national newspapers in the UK and US. Editor of the *Lebanon Daily Star* at various times since 1984, Middle East correspondent of the *London Daily Express* and a freelance writer, his heart is firmly anchored in Beirut. A devotee of *sawda nayyeh* (raw liver) and *arak* for breakfast, he claims to be Almaza's best customer and one of *Time Out*'s most loyal habitués.

MICHAEL KARAM has lived in Lebanon since 1992. He is a business journalist and wine writer. His articles have appeared in *Esquire*, *The Spectator*, *Decanter*, *Harpers* and *Wine Weekly*. He is a contributor to the award-winning *Wine Report* (Dorling Kindersley) and the *Oxford Companion to Wine* (Oxford University Press). He is author of *Wines of Lebanon* (Saqi), which won the Gourmand Award for the Best New World Wine Book 2005; *Chateau Ksara: 150 years of wine making 1957-2007* and *Arak and Mezze: The Taste of Lebanon* (Saqi), which will be published in 2007. He says that living in Lebanon has done nothing for his mental health.

A Fine Arts graduate, MAYA FIDAWI is striving once again to put a smile on our faces; only this time, she's not alone: her baby-to-be is joining her with kicks and bounces, anticipating to meet all these characters for himself pretty soon. So Lebanon, look out, a new artist is in the making. And last but not least, it is worth noting that all this would have never been made possible, had it not been for her beloved husband's support and inspiration.

Graphic designer REEM ABOU CHACRA who moved to New York City with her husband, now found her true *true calling*. And no, it is not book design -like we had thought- it is motherhood indeed! Now proud mommy to a gorgeous baby girl, Reem seems to have discovered the joyful meaning of life. Design, which used to be her baby, has now become *just design*.

10

Enjoy...

Gym Fanatic

Part of the mutual non-aggression pact between Rana and her husband of 15 years was that he never complained about or even questioned her simultaneous membership at Beirut's top two sports and fitness clubs. (In return, she never inquired about his whereabouts on Tuesday afternoons.) But there was a method to Rana's seeming madness. The two-hour sessions of Nautilus machine torture each Monday, Wednesday and Thursday were to get her in shape for the highlight of her week - an evening of pilates at her second sports club, under the oh-so-French personal direction of Marcel, 76 kilos of well-proportioned manhood from the tiny seaside town of Ault in Picardie. The bizarre habit of getting in shape before attending a fitness class was a practice she learned from her mother, who would have the maid clean her home from top to bottom before allowing in the contract cleaners at the beginning of each month. Thus Rana's dedication to the cause of getting in perfect shape allowed her to parade her toned and mildly muscular, though feminine, body in the front row of Marcel's weekly session. The immaculate, hour-old, $200 hairstyle at the beginning of each lesson put her apart from the rest of the class, as did the quality of her sportswear. Nothing flashy, revealing or vulgar like what those younger women wore. Yet the conservative (if almost snug fitting) outfit broadcast to the world at large, and Marcel in particular, the success of his system. And the crowning touch in demonstrating her devotion and sacrifice to him was seen in her dishevelled locks at the end of a session and her sexily perspiring but radiant face. Oh happy Rana, that she could fantasise about what he was thinking as he paid his star pupil extra attention, bestowing on her the kindest and gentlest of smiles. Oh happier still that she never learned of his late-night workout sessions with his boyfriend.

-PG

Online Dater

To hell with Lebanese men! Who needs them and their macho hang ups? Rima is 30 and single and all her family are muttering that she's still unmarried. She had a close shave with her 4th cousin twice-removed, who, according to her aunt, "worked at a bank, had 16 months salary and could get an easy mortgage." Yeah, but he was also overweight, balding, had death breath and, tellingly enough, carried a nail clipper key chain. *A-ba-dan.* She heard about online dating in a magazine she read at *De Belgrade* coffee house in Hamra and immediately popped into the nearest internet café. Within half an hour she - or, should we say, *DeliciousBeirutBabe* - had been propositioned for cyber sex a dozen times - mostly by Indonesian men - and had caught the eye of a Viennese lesbian who wanted to fly her out to Austria that weekend. Still, Rima persevered and is now in an intriguing online relationship with Barry, a British plumber - AKA *leak_plugger* - from Croydon. He likes her exotic looks - they have exchanged photos - and "rare sense of family," while she admires the fact he left home at 18. Ah yes... he is married. She does not want to think about that too much, though, and in the meantime she's also "seeing" Bob, a highway patrolman from Texas, and Dayo, a Nigerian student in Istanbul. Barry has told her he loves her. She said it back. Why not? He is a real man with a real life and a proven commitment to family. He sends constant text messages and her relatives can't understand why she sits all alone in the corner on Sunday evening smiling at her cellphone. No wonder she never married, they confide.

-MK

Plastic Surgeon

Fond of both the good life and beautiful women, Charles made himself a promise at the end of a five-year medical internship in Wichita. He would have his own reasonably good looks surgically enhanced, to become a kind of walking advertisement for the cosmetic surgery business he planned to set up once back in Kaslik. And rapidly, he discovered he couldn't fail. The young wanted to look older; the old wanted to look younger; the fat sought to be thinner and the flat-chested to be curvy. With his charm, his handsome appearance and a small but extravagantly furnished, $10,000-a-month consulting suite, Charles launched into the business of becoming seriously rich. Ironically, the first series of operations - nose, breasts, buttocks - were performed free of charge on his receptionist. Not perfect - his paying clients had to look better than Samia - but certainly good enough to be a permanent front-of-house billboard. At the beginning, he made his money out of cute little noses (sometimes up to 80 a week) and pert (but not-so-little) breasts. Charles had always been a perfectionist, if somewhat limited in scope and imagination. Although they never seemed to notice, all the women were becoming cosmetic clones of each other. Even so, as his reputation grew along with his clients' chests, women and even men flooded in from throughout the region. One female client he viewed as a particular professional triumph. Over three years, he had remodelled her from head to toe - eyes, cheeks, chin, breasts, tummy, buttocks, thighs. Charles was so proud of his achievement that he asked her to marry him. It was only on their honeymoon, as he caressed her flawless body, that he realised he hadn't actually married a woman - he had married his job.

-PG

Marriage Fixer

Kids these days! They just don't know what is good for them. Rose is widowed and spends her days introducing desperate men to women who don't want to get married and are happy riding on the back of a motorcycle with a nightclub owner. Rose just can't understand why her niece Shadia did not even want to meet Jamil. He works in Sweden. He has a nice house and a good job. He is educated and he is from a good family (why does Shadia always say, "Everyone seems to be from a good family. I'd like just for once to meet someone who is from a really awful family"?) and his father is leaving him a building on the road to Mansourieh. It's perfect. Shadia always talks nonsense about getting to know someone. We have the rest of our lives to get to know people! Did Rose know her husband before they married? No, but she got to know him and his habits (some good and some, well, less good) and they eventually settled into marital drudgery. But this poor boy has come all the way from Sweden and the least Shadia can do is sit with him. Ok, he is a bit of a *taboosh*, but she told Shadia if he is unhealthy it will be her responsibility as his wife. How ungrateful. She just hung up the phone. She should at least meet him. Rose really doesn't know what her brother did in raising that girl. People today fill their heads with love. Love won't pay the bills. Love won't bring a duplex apartment over a half-empty shopping center.

-MK

Mobilet Driver

Mustapha was a born driver - and survivor. He had been borrowing mini motorbikes since he was five. Sometimes he borrowed them from people he knew; sometimes, from people he'd like to have known. Despite barely being able to see over the handlebars, hours of practice made his masterful body-and-bike swerve the envy of the other kids on the block. By the time he was a teenager - and still "borrowing" other people's two-wheelers - he was rescued from a life of full-time crime by his cousin Mahmoud: he was equipped with his own Mobilet to deliver "Mikes Massiv Pizas." No one really minded that Mahmoud couldn't spell, but Mustapha wasn't much of a reader, which presented a more practical problem. At first he had to ring every buzzer in a building until the right person answered for the order. Yet, once learned, he never forgot where any of Mahmoud's customers lived nor their menu favourites. And those years of perfecting his wheelie were now really paying off. Mustapha did his job with panache: paid according to the number of deliveries, he soon learned how to carry an extra three pizza boxes on the fingertips of one hand while using the other to exercise some vague control over the bike as he weaved his way through traffic on one wheel. The fastest service in town had only one slight drawback: the pizzas had been thrown around so much over the journey that by the time they arrived, there was more topping on the lid of the box than the crust. But no one ever complained. The speed rush-induced, exhilarated smile on Mustapha's face as he handed over the soggy boxes was too disarming.

-PG

Bridge Player

Nahla is totally obsessed. Her day begins with the maid bringing her coffee in bed, where she sits with her new Powerbook (so cute in silver) and plays online bridge. It was not always thus. She joined the local club because she was bored in her marriage and needed a diversion. There she could meet like-minded men, men she could have married had she not listened to her parents (i.e. men who did not think life was a Porsche Cayenne, a Brietling and a Cohiba), sensitive souls who needed mental stimulation while their wives shopped and epilated. Just like André, all tortoise shell glasses, white button-down Oxford, Ralph Lauren Chinos and blazer. He oozed old money, which always helps. When his bridge partner died in surgery (liposuction has risks, too), Nahla was as tenacious in her pursuit of him as she was shrewd in her bidding. She wanted to show him she was no palooka, and the chemistry across (and under) the baize was white hot. Then there was the matter of the bridge club's annual trip to Istanbul... hmm, the Bosphorus. She felt like a young girl again, trying to sit near him on the coach; oh-how-coincidental that they were the last to leave the bar at the end of the first evening. André told her this was a difficult position for him, as traditionally, he never under-bids. "You won't this time, either," she swooned, purring that she was strong in hearts. It seemed to do the trick.

-MK

Fisherman

Zeinab could almost have taken it better if he'd found another woman. But to be abandoned night after night for a three-and-a-half meter wooden boat was an insult. Yet Abou Lina was a good man. His part-time jobs at the tiny fisherman's port - fixing other people's boats, cars, anything with a plug on it - brought in enough money to send their four girls to a private school. But a successful night's fishing, especially in the tuna season, was like winning the lottery. With so much time spent aboard his floating home-away-from-home, Abou Lina upgraded his 25-year-old craft with conveniences that put it, in his eyes, on par with the luxury yachts moored just 100 yards away. The small butane gas ring sufficed to cook his early morning meal and to heat coals for the *nargileh* he had specially delivered from Cairo. The *nargileh* itself was anchored in a metal box affixed to the deck. It really wouldn't do to cause a fire in the middle of the Med. A toolbox in case his own boat needed fixing, fishing lines and bait and a supply of fresh water (plus a few beers) almost completed the good ship's inventory. But the masterstroke was Abou Lina's addition of a slightly battered golf umbrella. At night, it sheltered him from the occasional rains (and kept his *nargileh* glowing); in the early morning, it helped to shield his eyes from the piercing rays of the rising sun; and at times of dire emergency, when all the contents of his toolbox and the complete repertoire of Abou Lina's ingenuity failed on the ancient engine, it could be adapted into a sail to get him safely back to shore - even if it wasn't always quite the bit of shore he wanted.

-PG

NGO Girl

Mary-Beth has come to Lebanon to work for an aid organisation. She is full of love and has huge hopes for the country, especially the poor impoverished people of the South. They are so decent, although she did have a minor "moment" with Ali, from Bint Jbeil. Initially, she had been mesmerised by his beauty, his purity, his love for family and his desire to advance himself. Shame about the desire bit. My god, she never meant to be friends *that* way. In any case, she is saving herself for Freddy, a South Korean co-worker she met in Jordan, another country where the people are so pure and simple (come to think of it, they were also like that in Yemen, Sudan and the Gaza Strip...maybe she just likes people?). She has already found an apartment for the two of them. The landlord was cool at first, them not being married and all, but when she started going to church, he warmed up. She just hopes he has nothing against Asians like her parents do, constantly warning her of the stress of having a mixed-race baby. In fact, it was these kinds of attitudes that drove her to the Middle East in the first place. Oh well, at least there is Spinneys next door (of course, she initially planned to live somewhere a bit more *authentic* than Ashrafieh - but it's just so convenient!). She and Freddy will shop together and carry the groceries home like regular people. Then there is the nice German couple under them - though she thinks they belong to a sect, which is a bit worrying, given her own beliefs. She often thinks of Ali and wishes that Freddy would arrive soon to banish the thoughts.

-MK

Local Journalist

The defining moment was the late morning launch of a new credit card. Illness at the office had given young Omar his first opportunity to attend a press gathering in a smart hotel. Apart from practicing his chat-up lines on the PR juniors, Omar also ate one of the best meals of his unadventurous life. To his surprise, the work part was very easy - a press kit in three languages ensured that. All he had to do was copy out what the PR people had written and put his name on the top. The publication of their releases word-for-word guaranteed personal invites to product launches from a growing number of PR firms. And all the launches, naturally, were accompanied by varying qualities of free food and drink. Occasionally, small gifts were included as a gesture of appreciation; memories of paying for the movies grew distant as invitations to pre-launch screenings poured in. All the while, Omar was faithfully reporting what the PR companies told him - though occasionally, he might ask a few hard-hitting questions like, "Could you please tell me the background on such a successful product?" How they loved him! He rapidly progressed to the price list menu. A discreet hint that if the flow of "news" from the PR firms continued to be published, he would receive a small cash gift for each one - and he was soon doubling his salary. Ironically, as his income rose, his daily expenses declined because so much free food was on offer. It also didn't really matter if he understood what was going on or not. As long as someone provided words, he would pass them on for inclusion. Soon came the trips abroad to regional product launches, long weekends at holiday destinations (no need to write about the place - articles of all sizes were available from the trip organisers) and high-tech gifts of growing proportions. "Informing the world is such a profitable job," mused Omar. "I wonder if those political reporters know what they're missing?"

-PG

Domestic Dog Walker

The arrival of a miniature pincher named Lassie into her life has given Cory the nightly opportunity to meet up with all her other friends whose employers bought dogs as accessories and now loathe them. When madam walked into the kitchen that morning and trod on the *kaka* that Cory could have cleared up but didn't, her ticket to freedom was assured. Now they all gather on one street corner and chat for at least an hour ("But madam, if he doesn't do his business, it will make trouble at home!"), offering up a silent prayer of thanks to the patron saint of dog walking. The salon owner used to get very mad about all the mess outside, especially when Mrs. Karam had that accident, but then madam, who uses the salon, bought the pooper-scooper. Sundays are a big problem for madam and mister because they have to walk the dog themselves and they never get it right; when Cory comes back from her church group, they are so happy to see her because Lassie has been a very bad boy. There was also the incident when Lassie got Snoopy the doberman pregnant - Mr. Fawaz came round to complain and there was a lot of trouble. Madam's daughter hates Lassie and once tied him to the back of the neighbor's GM Suburban. Sensing that her ticket to walk would be lost forever, Cory intervened. A tiny Burberry coat and hat were bought to repair the trauma to poor Lassie's psyche. Now all the dogs have them.

-MK

Professor

The prestige of being a professor was terrific. Obviously, Fawaz was intelligent, but he was also witty, charming, articulate and attractively free of ostentation. His brown corduroy jacket - regulation uniform of the professor of political science - had seen better days, but Fawaz always knew he was admired for his mind, not for his wardrobe. A man of the people, he was adored by his students and gladly repaid their devotion by joining them at times for lunch in the cafeteria. His three books had received rave reviews over the years, his lectures were well-attended and he was regularly interviewed by the local press, radio and TV. He had fame (or at least, he was gaining it). It was fortune - the financial recognition his brains deserved - that proved elusive. Until the day of the phone call. Would he care to speak at a conference in the Gulf? Business-class travel (with the accompanying free drinks in airport lounges), five-star accommodation and a $1,000 fee for his speech. That Gulf gathering became the catalyst for redressing all the missing materialism in Fawaz's life. One good speech was the passport to more and better-paid appearances throughout the Middle East, Europe and North America. And, of course, his wife was invited as well. A new publisher in London was offering bigger advances on his books, now thought worthy of translation into several languages. The US university lecture circuit opened up, and Fawaz began to spend more time on the road than he did with his students in Beirut. The one element that didn't change was his uniform: the brown jacket that identified him and established his credentials as an academic was a permanent fixture, with its accompanying slightly baggy trousers and battered brown shoes. His only indulgence was to add a collection of bow ties befitting a man of his intellect. After all, this was show business.

-PG

SUV Lady

Life is so hectic for Karine. Thank goodness the maid, Imelda, can get the kids ready for school - they all grow up so fast these days - and take care of the dog, a Belgian thingy that she just had to have after Killer, her Pekinese, died of cancer. Really, Imelda is a dear and she has a degree, which if the truth be told, is more than Karine has, but shh! Enough! Naughty boy! Seriously though, the Lexus has made life so much easier. One day it was ok to drive an American 4x4, the next, unless it was German, you were garbage. Ok, that was a minor setback and she got on Tony's case straightaway, screaming that she did not marry him to drive around in a Cherokee and be laughed at. In fact, come to think of it, she only married him because he had money coming out of his ears. And if she couldn't use the money, what was the point? Certainly not to visit his barbaric family in Kinshasa every year. No, it had to be a Lexus. Ahh. The balance of nature was restored when she handed the keys to the doorman at *Teez*. Ok, Tony will still have to drive his 2003 Jaguar for a few years, but a man must make sacrifices for the well-being of his family. Nabil will be 18 soon and he will need a Hummer if he is to get anywhere in this crazy town, and then their daughter will want something too. Sometimes she wonders if Tony ever takes his duties as a father seriously.

-MK

Politician's Son

From his earliest memory, Samir was aware that his father was different from other men. After all, other kids saw their dads first thing in a morning and then perhaps not until they woke up the following day. Samir saw his father all the time, on the TV news, the political chat shows and sometimes in advertisements for his party. There was even a photo of them both together in father's study. That proved rather fortunate, as it helped them recognise each other on the odd occasion when the family ate together. Dad was obviously a very important man - and rich too - because Samir had a bodyguard and chauffeur-driven Cadillac from his first days at school. Now in his late teens and sporting a more youthful version of his father's trademark - if dyed - black moustache, Samir has learned to use his favoured status to advantage. On trips to Beirut's "Silicone Valley" beach club, he is surrounded by male friends who see Samir as an entrée to the Great Man's patronage and bikinied beauties who are more in awe of the size of his spending power than that of his other assets. Outside bars and night clubs, parking spaces magically appear at the approach of the big black car while inside, tables are cleared of lesser mortals to accommodate his party of good-looking hangers-on. So different from the lonely days of his early teens when the chauffeur was instructed to find, approve and pay for suitable dates. Now he is the centre of attention and girls just flock to him. The chauffeur still pays their expenses, of course.

-PG

Traffic Cop

Toufic's job isn't so bad. They have given him a corner where he stands every day. He has his regular customers and because this is one of Beirut's most prestigious roads, they pay very well. Ok, it was better when the Hollywood theme restaurant was there (because then he could also tap into the parking business) but that has gone and so has the revenue stream. He likes to think they respect him not because of the gun he packs - oh, no - but because of the medals he was awarded for good service. What did he do? Well, he can't remember really - but now he has his own patch and he is doing very nicely, thank you. Women looking to park are his favorite. Yes, he is quite the charmer and the way he wears them down is something of an art. He knows they all secretly like him, but he is a family man. Anyway, what are a few thousand lira to them? They go and spend millions at lunch, so they can afford it, and after all, rules are rules. They are not allowed to park here. Official cars can do what they want, why not? He has to play the game. Would he stop a minister for speeding? Is he mad? A minister is a very important person and might be in a hurry. Does he respect them? Why not? They have money but they are all as bad as each other. If the truth be told, this is a filthy country, *maheyk?*

-MK

Martyrs' Square Demonstrator

Peter's mother wasn't too keen on the idea of his camping out in Martyrs' Square. Surely if he wanted to protest something, he could do it at that good university they pay $15,000 a year for him to attend. Why risk getting involved in a place where there were hundreds of security forces? Heaven forbid, he might even get arrested. Dad was more pragmatic about Peter's debut into street politics. After all, if the need arose, his parents had plenty of weapons at their disposal to bring Peter home - like revoking the keys to his new car. Peter himself knew he was being idealistic by expecting to be part of a movement that would change the country, but he wanted to be able to say he tried. Once inside the (good-quality, Gulf-supplied) tent, he recognised, already installed in a corner and preaching to his neighbours, the black sheep cousin from his mother's side of the family. From behind Marwan's untended beard emerged a string of arguments lauding the new communism as the way ahead. Peter had never been able to stand Marwan's lefty firebrand politics, but this was what the tent was all about - defending his own brand of designer-stubble democracy against any and every alternative. Every evening, Peter's mum sent in enough freshly cooked food to fuel the entire tent for the night-long debates. By the dim light of a (lesser-quality, Chinese-built, but still Gulf-supplied) torch, they talked till daylight, mapping out a new dawn for the country. So it continued for weeks until the campers determined that, following the incarceration of some leading figures they thought should be in jail and the release of a few others they thought shouldn't, their work was done and it was time to go home. Their contribution to peaceful revolution had been made and practical politics could be laid aside. Someone else could run the country now.

-PG

Old Foreign Correspondent

The bearded and bedraggled Helmut has been in the Middle East for over 30 years and has covered every war - Iran, Iraq, Iraq II, Iraq III, Iraq IV, Palestine, even Somalia and Ethiopia. He has interviewed Benazir Bhutto ("a babe") and the "guy that got whacked by that bomb" (he forgets his name). In fact, there is not much that Helmut can remember. (Can you blame him? War does that to a man.) He married an Iranian who works for an NGO, a state of affairs that leads Helmut to wander around Ras Beirut muttering about the good old days when Arafat ran the show. His primary interest lately is missiles and other armaments, a subject upon which he is now considered something of an expert. But when he is not writing for specialist magazines - *Cluster Bomb Quarterly* is always happy to receive copy from Helmut - he goes to his favorite pub in a side street near the Ministry of Economy, where he and the owner swap war stories over vast quantities of *arak*. Occasionally, he will get a phone call from an old colleague who has gone on to greater things and who invites him out on the expense account. The evening begins well enough, but the more they (well, Helmut) drink, the bitterer Helmut becomes. The night usually ends with Helmut telling the guy to go f**** himself and that he never liked him anyway. He staggers home (waking up the concierge even though he has the key) where his wife gives him a restorative *arak* and tells him that *Bazooka* wants 2,000 words on Israeli mortar tactics. He is loved; he is in demand and tomorrow is another day.

-MK

Beach Club Mother

Sandra has done pretty well. After a year of close encounters with a well-connected if not particularly well-endowed Mr. 15%, her efforts were rewarded with a CLK Cabriolet that turns even more heads than her blonde highlights and the seductive-yet-classy necklines of most of her wardrobe. It hadn't been difficult marrying the older millions. He gets to parade her at official receptions; she gets to replace her Mercedes every summer. Working out with a personal trainer had returned the sleek appearance of her own chassis following the two children her husband's money deserved (well, demanded really). But for Sandra, sun-worshipping now takes a little more organisation: she has to somehow balance the hard, important work of maintaining a perfect tan with motherhood. On the way to the beach, her driver follows a discreet kilometre behind in the Discovery while she pilots the CLK down the coast. His cargo consists primarily of maid, children and a boot full of equipment to keep them amused; hers is a hundred grand's worth of jewellery on each arm. Sandra transfers the kids to her car a few minutes from the beach - this strategy is good on arrival for her reputation of doting mother, but offers minimal risk of their dirtying the seats. Inside the club, Sri Lankan Melanie feeds, plays with and calms the little ones while madam divides her time between evenly tanning her bikinied body, like a chicken on a slowly-turning spit, and sipping cold drinks with her friends in the shade of a giant parasol. Melanie doesn't have a chance to sit - but there's no chair for her anyway. Her function is to make sure the children don't interrupt Sandra's afternoon and to be waiting by the side of the pool with robe, soft towel and fresh swimwear after madam's dip. Back home and recounting the details of the children's day to their father, Sandra observes that being a mother is tiring and a tremendous responsibility. But it's worth it to see the smiles on their little faces.

-PG

The Concierge

Seeri is from Sri Lanka. He has been concierge at the Havana Building for five years. He thinks - and has told his family back home - that he now speaks Arabic, but it is in fact a hybrid of Arabic, French, and English with a few words of Armenian (courtesy of Mrs. Kouyoumjian on the 1st floor). In fact, you could say he speaks Lebanese. The tenants all treat him pretty well - apart from the Khourys, who have three cars but only space for one and who just park anywhere and who demand he walk the dog and carry in the shopping and bring their paper and who give him the smallest tip at Christmas. Still, at least he gets to drive the cars and it cheers him up to know that he isn't that careful about knocking the doors against the concrete pillars when he opens them. His sister works for the family on the 4th floor and they make sure he gets all the old clothes. In fact, he dresses quite well. He has Façonnable shirts, Florsheim shoes and Polo jeans among other goodies. Mr. Gemayel was quite shocked when he noticed that they were wearing the same shirt one day. The tenants were very nice after the tsunami, and Mrs. Kerbage even baked a cake for his family back home in Sri Lanka. Most recently, the Norwegian family on the 5th floor donated an aquarium full of tropical fish when they left the country, but the fish died within a month and now the tank sits in the entrance hall, empty except for a plastic starfish, a peeing cherub and a dozen cigarette ends.

-MK

Maître D'

Blessed with a name to match his ambition, Jean-Louis was determined to better the living his father had made as a waiter at *La Brasserie de Versailles*. Even as a child at the annual family lunch (on a wintry Wednesday when the restaurant was likely to be empty anyway), Jean-Louis could tell how hard all the staff tried to cultivate an air of Frenchness. The tips were bigger if the real customers on other days could be transported for a couple of hours to the Champs-Elysées. After a few years learning the trade as a waiter, Jean-Louis' chance to shine came with the opening of *Le Café Royal*. Not yet 30, he became one of the youngest top-notch maîtres in the city. He acquired half a dozen suits so he could wear freshly laundered clothes each lunch and dinner time. (The last thing his well-heeled customers needed was a maître who smelled of food.) Jean-Louis learned just enough about wine to impress everyone except those who were well-versed in vino themselves (and then he knew to shut up). But his masterstroke - or maître-stroke - as he saw it was keeping up with the capital's news and gossip, always aware of who among his wealthy diners was trying to contact whom, and equally, who was trying to avoid whom. Strangers rash enough to stray into Le Café Royal were automatically directed to tables by the window, in order to preserve the regulars' delicate seating arrangement. Meanwhile, Jean-Louis was busily influencing the nation's politics, finance, business and even love-lives by his judicious choice of places for his clients to eat. With more than a handful of tables greasing his palm with $20 or $50 daily to be close to (or far from) specific diners, Jean-Louis could easily have financed his own restaurant. But why abandon a good business?

-PG

School Run Mom

Babs met her husband Philippe at university in Boston, where she thought he was French (so elegant and neat, unlike those disgusting frat boys) and it was only after six months of denial that she realised he was Lebanese. Her parents were initially skeptical of the union, but when Philippe got a job with JP Morgan in Paris they figured he was ok. As her father put it, "the kid ain't gonna fly a 747 into his own office now, is he?" Moving to Lebanon was a wrench, but she soon realised they have SUVs over here too and Philippe got a good job and after a while it was just like the States: the kids, the school run, the book club, coffee with friends, the gym, light lunch and a bit of shopping. Then she got involved in writing a kids' book. Bret and Stevie's Arabic was so weak and she wanted them to be as smart as Philippe, who was by now rapidly rising at the bank. She tells him it's because he worked abroad and got that MBA. Still, her parents won't visit even though they keep on saying they will "next year." Yes, sometimes she gets lonely, especially when men think she is one of those Russian girls that come and give foreign wives a bad name. Philippe always talks about Lebanon being a place of family values and closeness. She just wishes his brother would stop harassing her, maybe it's because she told him that her family was originally from Eastern Europe. Those girls have a lot to answer for.

-MK

Vegetable Vendor

None of Moussa's regular customers were ever quite sure where he came from. Certainly his small collection of fruit and vegetables was always fresh and of good (if not the finest) quality. His prices were too modest to ever be worth negotiating and the deft way he manoeuvred his ageing wooden trailer put him in the same class as those service drivers who know the width of their ancient Mercedes to the centimetre. But what really set Moussa apart was the way he made himself indispensable. Come rainstorm or heatwave, he appeared on exactly the same corners at exactly the same time every day, except Sundays, when he arrived precisely two hours later. Nor did the 20 minutes he stayed at his chosen spots ever vary. Moussa had the weathered face that came with being outside all day, every day, and a slight, sparsely toothed smile that alternated with expressions of intense concentration on what was going around him. If anyone had noticed or cared, they would have seen that Moussa's good fruit and good service wasn't really what he was interested in. He knew the inhabitants of nearly every apartment in the area, when they changed their cars, which vehicles were strange to the neighbourhood and the faces of the regular visitors from other parts of town. Hidden away under the scales and unseen by most of his clients were two soundless cellular phones. He was a man who used his mouth and his ears in the same proportion that nature had endowed him. He listened twice as much as he spoke. In fact, it was hearing a short discussion between two neighbours that convinced him to begin displaying a Lebanese flag wedged into one corner of the trailer next to the bananas.

-PG

Commercial Airline Pilot

When Habib qualified, his grandmother asked him what kind of job this was. Surely he was nothing more than a flying *service* driver. "Is that what you want people to think of you?" she had demanded, when he came to see her for the first time in his uniform. But he had it all planned out. What other job offered him such power? What other job allowed him to be served a cognac and given a neck massage as he taxied the plane after landing. Then there were the women, the hotels and the duty free. The job has given him a taste for wine and cigars and -- this is very important -- people call him "Captain." Of course, the quick turnarounds have changed things a bit, there's less time to show around the first officer and have fun. Then again, the job has also allowed him to embark on business ventures. Habib opened *Charlie Foxtrot*, a pub in Jounieh which is doing ok (though his pilot buddies expect to drink for free). Since 9/11, everything is different. Now you can't invite girls into the cockpit, even though he makes exceptions. And all this talk about pilots being armed - what's new? He has kept a Klashen under his seat for years. His first officer is in love with a head flight attendant. He tells him he is missing the whole point behind being a pilot. Why marry into the airline? When she retires to have children, she will know how the system works. No, no, no! That's not the reason you become a Captain.

-MK

Sporting Club Devotee

Jamila knows the Sporting Club as well as her own home. A member since birth, she was brought up to recognise the territorial rights of the members of her parents' generation, as well as their eccentricities. Like Marwan, who spends 90 minutes a day walking the perimeter of the club, with exaggerated thrusts of the elbows to show his commitment to serious exercise. Unthinkable to park a lounge chair on his route. Or Hind, whose ration of two small bottles of water before six and two large sandwiches after illustrates the schizophrenia besetting her 73 kilos. But who cares? And Emile, whose recliner is assured its precise spot halfway along the inlet on the far side, whether he is present or not. This is Sporting, where sworn enemies hand in their hang-ups at the entrance and the beautifully big let it all hang out. Not that Jamila's fat and flabby. A little oversize, maybe, but there's solid muscle in her short frame, the product of regular swims throughout the afternoon and early evening. Jamila is also the kind whose perfect dives into the sea three meters below put to shame the men who nervously hang around, summoning the courage to jump in feet first. And no need for her to waste vast sums on the latest swimwear (ok, *solderie* offerings maybe) or accessories to disguise a spreading rear. Occasional visitors who arrive expecting to see Perfect Lebanese Women have obviously come to the wrong place. It's towards the end of a day that it's easiest to spot the other long-time habitués of that U-shaped concrete paradise. Almost in unison, without fuss and with just enough noise to let strangers know the ritual is about to begin, the old hands gently turn their plastic loungers due west to pay daily homage to the sunset.

-PG

Beggar

Begging isn't what it used to be. There was a time when Sayeed made a decent living delivering gas canisters and carrying shopping bags upstairs for the elderly residents of his neighborhood in Hamra. But then Abou Reeshi went and spoiled all that by being unmasked as a spy (and to think that they shared the same cardboard box for three years!). After that, everyone suspected Sayeed was a spy, too. You would think Abou Reeshi, or whatever his name really was, might have taken him with him. Anyway, after his cardboard house was burnt down Sayeed saw no reason to stay in Hamra, so he moved to Ashrafieh and then Dora, where he pretended to be legless. It earned him about LL20,000 a day (some of which went towards paying off the loan for the specially cut-back rubber boots that allowed him to look like he walked on stumps and tell people he had been run over by a drunk Arab playboy). But the cops saw his feet sticking out of the back of the boots and so it was either jail or splitting his earnings with them. He has realised that strategic alliances are good. For his 50/50 arrangement, he has a free rein from Dora to Antelias. The construction of the new bridge has led to snarling traffic and greater pickings. Sayeed has an uncanny knack for knowing who will fork out. Harassed women, fat, middle-aged men and Arab tourists are his best 'marks,' but the young men with flags who drive around on Sundays try to run him over. Where are the police when you need them?

-MK

Part-Time Designer

The first person to recognise Serene's talents was her father. After all, he funded her painting lessons as a child. Indeed, he became so interested in the world of art that shortly before her teenage competition entry was highly commended, he donated $5,000 to the organising institute. After acquiring - in similar vein - a degree in fine arts, Serene attended some of a 12-month course on Freehand, Photoshop and Quark Xpress so she could follow dad's advice and share her gifts with the world of business and commerce. A job with RtisTique Designs was assured (that's where Serene's father placed his corporate business). Nothing too strenuous - starting sometime before 11, to give her a few hours each morning to perfect the casual, bohemian look that suited a successful artist. And finishing not too long after lunch so Serene could avoid heavy traffic on the way home. The only way RtisTique owner Marcel could get rid of her and keep her father's business was to say he needed her to work on so many accounts she simply had to put in a full six-day week. With that out of the question, she turned to accepting one-off commissions. Dad had no qualms about telling his friends and company suppliers how much she was in demand, so her order book was rapidly running over with requests to create corporate identities for planned new companies. Her software for generating logos from company initials and CD libraries of images guaranteed she could always dash off something, even if it was of childlike simplicity. Everyone was happy. Her clients added the equivalent of her fees to bills they submitted to her father. Dad felt the glow of satisfaction from having helped the talented apple-of-his-eye launch a career. And Serene? Far too busy to notice that everyone paid for her work but nobody ever used it.

-PG

Rich Kid Restaurant Owner

The idea seemed fool-proof. Henry would get 20 friends to put up $5,000 each. He would rent the premises, hire a chef (you can get them for next to nothing... *balesh*) and by his calculations would be $50k richer by the end of the summer, at which point he would close it down. People are so stupid, they will pay to eat anywhere... so he thought. Even the name, *Octopussy*, would make it a hit with the ladies who lunch. He could hear it now. "Yee! We went to *Octo'*. *C'est tres mignon!*" Well, yes, again, that was the idea. As it turned out, he went through three chefs in the first month. He didn't know there could be a downside to *balesh*. A hair in a caesar salad brought the restaurant's name a bit too close to home, while an errant cockroach sent one famous lady luncher running into the street. Not a good start, and a situation hardly helped by friends of investors who expected to eat for free. Was he operating a restaurant or a soup kitchen? He didn't care if they were "bringing in business." Another mystery was why the seasonal university students (another segment of the workforce apparently happy to work for nothing) often failed to show up for their shifts. Still, he has just spotted a space in Gemmayzeh that would be perfect for his next "foolproof" venture. One day he might just get it right, and in the meantime, daddy is picking up the bill.

-MK

Sudoku Fanatic

For a man who had never shone at crosswords, sudoku seemed heaven-sent. Here was Walid's chance to show his stuck-up office colleague Salma that he was bright, too. For months, she had been polishing off one crossword in the morning coffee break, only to be seen demolishing a second set of clues during lunch. It wasn't just the speed with which she filled up the empty squares that rattled his cage. It was also the smug way she laid down the pen between each clue so the noise of snatching it up signalled she had found another answer. Determined to demonstrate he was equally smart, Walid took up sudoku. True, the solution to each square could only be one of nine numbers rather than any of 26 letters. True, the number of blank spaces was far fewer than in Salma's crossword. But it was still a mighty vehicle for parading his brainpower. He wouldn't be so childish as to throw the pencil down between numbers, yet he did take care to fold the paper with a flourish before sauntering off. Walid's problem came on days when the newspaper ran a "difficult" grid. The editors claimed it was at the readers' request. Certainly not this reader, thought Walid, as he watched Salma rattle through a 15x15 crossword while he was less than halfway to a solution. It was at that point his real genius surfaced. If he gave sudoku a miss for one day, he could memorise the solution from the following day's paper but take the earlier issue into work. After all, she would never notice since his paper showed only the puzzle. In this way, Walid conclusively proved day after day the superiority of his intellect. Until the morning Salma asked if she could look at the page with the TV listings...

-PG

Lebanese 'New Man'

Tony has come back to Lebanon after living in the US for 20 years. He met the formidable Angela at NYU. They dated, married and now have a three-month-old son, Shep (short for Shepherd, Angela's maiden name -- it was her idea). When they go out or travel, they are a veritable caravan of diapers and wipes and bottles and Tupperware containers. These days Angela's nipples are raw from Shep's vice-like clench, so Tony wears the baby sling. This provokes raucous comments from his brother and cousins - *shoo hayda ya Tony? System jdeed?* - all of whom are, in Tony's eyes, nothing more than "unreconstructed villagers" who have never washed a mug - let alone changed a diaper. His father, who was not prepared for Tony's enthusiastic adoption of the whole 'new man' thing, winces every time Angela barks orders about bottles or burping, and he buries himself in his paper when she flops out a breast at the table during meals. Tony hesitated before telling his parents that not only does he cook - he took lessons - but he and Angela have agreed that he should be a stay-at-home-dad, since her salary as an investment banker is triple his stipend as a sociology lecturer. He knew his father would greet this news with sneering disdain and use it to confirm his 1984 prediction that the degree would prove to be a complete waste of money. "So this is how it has turned out," he lamented when Tony broke the news. "You have stabbed me and your mother. Why can't you be like your brother George, who runs a money exchange?" Later that night, Angela called him a "wuss." He can't win.

-MK

Ras Beiruti Lady

The best lesson Fadia ever learned about her husband came when she wooed and won him in the first place. Her charms and a slender figure (more to the point, one not ravaged by four children in as many years) had helped her lure Ahmed away from his wife. Now that she has him and his connections, she plans to hang on to him. Slim, but in a womanly way, Fadia can pull off body-hugging fabrics that showcase her figure. She just doesn't have the taste to go with it. A misplaced affinity for nature seemingly motivates Fadia to dress in prints that make her resemble a cheetah at times, and a mutant zebra at others. If the fashion magazine said black and white were in style, she'd be right up there with the best. And the subtle accessories it speaks of, to add a touch of colour, style and class? She has gold bracelets of every kind - narrow, broad, jewelled, patterned, plain. Quite clearly, the more of them she wears at any given time, the more colour, class and style she will have. She gave Ahmed two children, rapidly regained her figure and has since brought them up by studiously ignoring them and throwing his money at their problems. After all, she has to look after the man who puts *foie gras* on her table, not the boy who puts greasy fingers on her clothes. She recently began to add other touches to her ever-more attention-grabbing appearance. The long cigarette holder (with gold bands and an amethyst) sets her apart from other women, as does the collection of designer handbags that never seem to match the spirit of her growing collection of black-and-white "animal" clothes. But the greatest sartorial triumph came when a saleswoman persuaded Fadia to have swimsuits made to match her favourite dresses. The same display of her taste... just smaller doses.

-PG

Young Foreign Correspondant

Sometimes when Teddy wakes up he can't remember where he is. Is this Dubai, Cairo, Baghdad, Ramallah or Damascus? The Middle East is a bit more confusing than life at his last job as a sports editor back in Boston. Goodness! Back then, he didn't know his *Sunni* from his *Shia*, but now people refer to him as a "veteran" and a "Mideast expert" even though he relies on Selma, his fixer, to do everything. And why didn't anyone tell him about Lebanon? He thought it was full of religious nuts running around killing each other. Man! The women in this town! And who said the place was dangerous? The only dangerous moment has been driving back over from the Bekaa after a particularly refreshing lunch at that fantastic little winery. Ok, there was the war. His editor told him to head down to Tyre. He had never heard of it, but Selma showed him on a map and Khaled the driver - suddenly on triple rate - drove them south. Funnily enough, all the correspondents he had met in every other Arab capital were there too, so he felt right at home at the hotel bar. He had a great sea view from his balcony, and he listened to the news reports to file his copy. The paper just needed a Tyre dateline, and he was under strict instructions not to get killed. After the war, a minister invited him to a dinner where the foreign press corps was thanked for its fair reporting. He had enough whisky to sink the Sixth Fleet and had to ask Selma - suddenly she was "darling Selma" - to remind him where he was and where he was headed the next day. Cairo? Oh, ok. He hates Cairo.

-MK

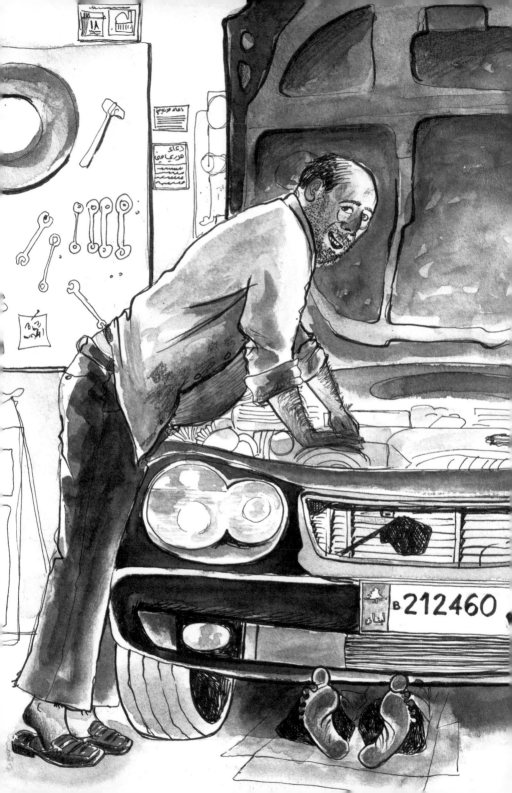

Local Mechanic

Abou Khaled's father was proud of his son's natural gift for fixing anything broken. As he progressed from household items to bicycles and eventually cars, the boy was obviously carving out an ability to make a living. Though the young mechanic was light on cash, brightening up the long-abandoned lock-up that housed his first premises was easy. An engine tune, brake adjustment and minor panel beating job for the owner of a paint store later, Abou Khaled was equipped to decorate his premises. Now all he needed were customers. Any temptation to copy the rest of the row of tiny car repair businesses by exaggerating a car's problems to its owner (and then triple-charging him) was crushed by his father's words of wisdom: "A cheated customer will quickly tell everyone how bad you are. Satisfied drivers will bring their friends." In his spare time, Abou Khaled took to learning tricks of his trade from the old hands in the neighbourhood and steering clear of his own age group (who rarely saw a return customer). His greatest triumph of ingenuity over engineering stemmed from one of these conversations. Faced with a cash-strapped customer whose car's back axle sounded like a bag of metallic bones, Abou Khaled rejected the notion of $600 plus labour for a new differential. "Come back tomorrow," he told the worried owner. "How much is it going to cost me?" asked the customer the following day. "Try it for a day," said Abou Khaled. "How much?" the delighted but still financially-wary owner repeated 24 hours later. "$25 for some very expensive oil," said the mechanic. "The bananas in your differential I'll throw in free of charge." The car performed perfectly for another 18 months before really needing a new back axle.

-PG

Gemmayzeh DJ

Marc still lives at home with his mother even though he is nearly 50. After breakfast, he watches reruns of *MASH* and likes to think he is a latter-day Hawkeye. He then heads to his favorite coffee shop, where he plays records on the turntable all afternoon. It helps him meet girls, who he hopes will find him funky and/or mysterious after he introduces them to '70s rock anthems and obscure trance records. Marc tells them stories from the civil war, especially about his camping trips to the North: "We just had to get out of the whole fighting scene, babe." The other day, the café owner had a word with him because he had gotten complaints that Marc was keeping people from enjoying their coffee in peace. What did he know about peace? That night, his mother told him that AUB had a vacancy for a porter. "It's a big organisation with job security." She just doesn't get it. His records are his life... well, what's left of it. She asks him if he has seen his ex-fiancée, who married the insurance claims adjuster. "She loved you more, but he had a career," she reminds him. Yes, he had seen her. There was an awkward moment in the street. What was she wearing? She looked so middle aged. Where did it all go wrong? The head shop he opened after the war failed, as did his plan to import those tie-dyed t-shirts. The gallery with Chico is all gone and now he has nothing in a country that offers nothing. Still, he has that piece of land in Batroun... and his records.

-MK

Ambassador's Wife

Sheila had it made when she was young. Tall, elegant, a grade A student: the kind of woman whose combination of brains and beauty left men weak at the knees, yet too intimidated to approach her. Maxwell's greatest achievement as he crawled up the Foreign Service had been to charm her into becoming what he saw as the perfect ambassador's wife. Four countries, fluency in Arabic and the requisite two children later, he reached the pinnacle of his ambition - the right to be called His Excellency the Ambassador. For Sheila, now in her early 50s, the trap door was closed tight. Forbidden as an envoy's wife to pursue the career her intellect demanded and essentially ignored by a husband who viewed her as little more than a public relations aide, she reached for the bottle. Even at the annual Ambassadors' Wives Charity Bazaar, she slipped a little something into her purse to fortify the tea and bolster her spirits. The seemingly endless cycle of visits to orphanages and women's collective jam-making enterprises was punctuated by the obligatory cocktail parties; most of the time, she found the guests as boring and cringe-worthy as her husband. But just occasionally, one of the male guests shared her passions for jazz, post-Impressionist art and conversation that rose above the level of flattery and small-talk in the rest of the room. Working hard to control the extra gin she wished she hadn't taken now that a potential soul mate had appeared on the scene, Sheila soon discovered she had not totally lost her natural ability to charm and entrance. Attractive as she still was (despite the odd alcohol-aided wrinkle), men's reactions were the same as when she was young. It was her brain-power, not her body that bewildered them. And in any case, it wouldn't be very diplomatic to come on strong to the ambassador's wife!

-PG

Bill Fighter

Wadih has got it down to a fine art. He will never try unless he is certain he can win. He learned the hard way with that English trade delegation: obviously, they felt that by allowing him to pay for 50 people at dinner, they would be honoring his traditional Arab hospitality. Never again. Now he selects his targets carefully - like Bernard, his mega-successful cousin over from Canada with his family. He always likes to go to the mountain restaurants and would never dream of letting Wadih pay for 30 people, so he is safe. Still, he must be careful. When the bill comes, Wadih makes a flapping gesture to the waiter and with one deft movement shields himself from the lunging Bernard, holding him back with one arm as he reads the bill. Bernard then gets up and outflanks him, so he swings the other way and turns to Bernard's wife Trish (whom he secretly likes) and makes a top-teeth-over-bottom-lip gesture while stroking his chin in a way that implies shame on her husband's antics. She will of course say that Wadih shouldn't pay, and this allows the Canadian cousin to rip the bill out of his hands. He can now implement phase two of the campaign, which is to act aggrieved and tricked and chase Bernard around the table. The scene descends into a comic farce in which Wadih has become the sympathetic character to Bernard's brashness. The trick is to extricate himself at just the right moment, so that he gains the support of the onlookers without making Bernard look bad. He has had plenty of practice.

-MK

Mr. Persistent

Fadi is a man who hears nothing he doesn't want to hear. In pursuit of a half-price boat, he calls the seller in the middle of lunch to ask, "Will you take $2,000 less?" The boat vendor explains that he is eating, and will talk to him later. To which Fadi replies, "What is your final price?" A couple of hours later, Fadi calls back; a price for the boat is negotiated. Immediately, Fadi asks: "Have you spoken to the lawyer?" The vendor observes that would be difficult since a price was only agreed upon seconds before. Fadi demands to know when the lawyer will call him. He is given the lawyer's number for use later and assured the transaction will happen in good time. In the late afternoon, he calls the firm and asks when the lawyer is going to contact him about the sale. "He's in a meeting," Fadi is told. He persists: "Will the lawyer call me today? I have a check and I'm really anxious to buy this boat." With promises that the lawyer will indeed contact him shortly, Fadi concludes his telephonic barrage for the day. But the following morning, he appears to have forgotten most of the previous day's conversations: he begins by calling to ask the vendor, "Will you take $1,000 less?" The vendor reminds him that they already agreed on a price, and that is final; Fadi, at length convinced by this argument, announces that he will expect a call from the lawyer later that day. After a meeting is fixed to complete the sale and exchange documentation, he visits the lawyers and opens by asking, "Will the owner take $2,000 less for a quick sale?" Fadi's next idea is that rather than transfer the registration to his name, he will pay for the boat, leave it in the present owner's name and simply receive written authorisation to use it permanently. Failing in that maneuver, he asks, "Will he accept to receive monthly payments?"

-PG

International Operator

Sonya believes she is part of the global telecom industry (well, she has been speaking to foreigners all over the world everyday for 35 years, so that must count for something). It's a steady job, and one that has called on her to serve her country in its darkest days. During the war, she was a vital link to the outside world - which included her brother in Sydney who would reverse the charges to the Lebanese government. Sonya has had the same desk since she started, but the colleagues have come and gone - kidnapped, blown up, suffered heart attacks - and now she is seen as something of a senior figure at the exchange. She lives on endless rounds of Arabic coffee, Winstons and *bizr*, all provided at first by Maroun, and now by Maroun's son, Charbel. Yes, people come and go, but the world keeps on talking. Anyway, her job is never boring. Sonya does more than connect lines; she connects people. She loves that moment when she tells a mother in Montréal that her son is calling - even though she knows he is asking for money - and feels a naughty thrill when a wife calls her husband abroad and she can tell he is not alone. Does she eavesdrop? Not intentionally. She addresses all callers as *ayni* and feels she is demonstrating her professional credentials by wearily announcing the country code (she knows every one by heart) before being given the number. She realises the era of direct dialing is nearing its end, and then she will retire. But the job will stay with her. She will never be able to hear someone mention London and not want to say *eh ayni, arbaa arbaa, ou baaden?*

-MK

Designer Baby Boutique Assistant

After just a year in the baby shop business, Nadine is proud of her ability to calculate instantly and to within $50 how much she can persuade pregnant women and doting dads-to-be to part with. Not that anything so crude as numbers enters the caring conversations about what the precious new arrival will need. Well, not at the beginning anyway. The choice, Nadine points out, is between this collection of strollers, cots, baby baths, high chairs and other accessories displayed in a warmly lit setting of domestic bliss. "These are French," she adds, throwing in that most communicative of keywords (which says they are also the most expensive). There's the fine quality and safety features of the three-gear stroller, with deluxe suspension, interchangeable seats and two hanging points for the all-important baby bag (not included and $80 extra). Then, looking straight at the man, she emphasises the extra convenience for mum to have three different kinds of cot as junior grows during the first six months. He can't afford to be seen as stingy when it comes to his wife's welfare; she can't admit that three days after being born, the baby will be passed over to the care of the Sri Lanki. And they don't dare even view the Italian collection (second-most expensive), let alone the Far-East junk piled up in the corner. An hour and a half later - and several thousand dollars lighter - the happy couple leaves as owners of a colour-coordinated swinging crib, an early cot, later cot, blankets, drawers, a stroller and a sample of almost everything in the store. As she bids them farewell, Nadine muses that she must be losing her touch - she'd estimated their spending power at $95 higher. If only they'd said yes to the $80 baby bag that matched the stroller.

-PG

Hummer Driver

Getting papa to buy the Hummer was a major coup for 18-year-old Marcel. His argument was that it was safer than most cars and fortunately his father picked one up cheaply from a bankrupt client, so everyone was happy. Or were they? What his dad did not expect was the reaction of the tenants in the building, who complained that the family had exceeded its allocation of parking spaces and that the car was blocking out sunlight in the entrance hall. And if it were only that! Two days after taking possession of his Hummer, Marcel drove back from a party at rooftop bar *Taupe* and straight into the 1980 Volvo belonging to the octogenarian Mr. Maalouf, who muttered: "I bought it from the company and not a dent in 25 years, and now this." Still, Marcel was instantly the most popular kid in his class. Dana, the girl with the longest legs in the school, who had ignored him for 10 years, proclaimed him her boyfriend. What he didn't realise was that this meant driving her up to Faraya every day during the war. His father began to notice that his son's choice of car was proving quite expensive. Not only was petrol going through the roof, he had neglected to insure the bloody thing. The inevitable happened when Marcel was driving down from the mountains and, attempting to reenact a maneuver from *Copz III*, tried to overtake three cars. He managed two but the third forced him off the road and into the shop front of a patisserie. No more Hummer and no more Dana, whose nose job had to be reset.

-MK

Foreign Hire Schoolteacher

Tall, slim and boyishly fresh-faced, Sean felt he had landed in paradise after a brush with near disaster. He was the respected Anglophone European - the favoured breed of foreigner and one of the school's "star" catches in its ongoing pursuit to justify the fees it sought from parents (who were becoming more used to asking what they were getting for their money). After all, anything imported just has to be better than the home-grown variety. Not that Sean's academic qualifications were astounding or his teaching record wholly exemplary. His colleague at a minor, mixed British public school had been caught and quietly dismissed for succumbing to the charms of a teenage pupil who was a little too interested in earning extra credit. So when Sean landed in Beirut with a tax free salary higher than his take-home pay in England, a school-funded apartment and a better status than he'd ever enjoyed, he buried the thought that he, too, had been close to disgrace and expulsion for going where no teacher ought to tread. Even so, it wasn't easy. Although the school required shirts with buttons up to the neck for its girl pupils, it didn't precisely stipulate how many of them had to be fastened. And that made it difficult for Sean to concentrate on imparting the finer points of Shakespearean tragedy to his teenage students. The 30-something-year-old Sean did eventually find a safeguard against the seduction techniques practiced by his daily drove of Delilahs, and it was completely unrelated to professional disgrace or being thrown out of the country. It was the day a drinking friend outlined the possibility of being shot through the head by a girl's relative that Sean regained control of his ardour.

-PG

Obituary Addict

Armed with a solid supply of cigarettes and a big pot of coffee, Marlene spends her mornings scanning the obituaries in the local press. It is a comforting ritual that begins with *Nahar, Safir* and then *L'Orient*. A notice in all three has a pleasing symmetry. Marlboro stuck firmly in her finger, she will first of all look to see if any "big" families have lost anyone. Failing that, she will scan the family names and see if anyone she has known during her long but shallow life has been affected by loss. If so - and if the service is not being held in some mountain bumpkin location - it will be the catalyst for a series of phone calls to the rest of the sentinels on the death-watch circuit. First of all, they will decide whether to go to the funeral service or just to the condolences. If they do go to the funeral, it allows them to show up for the lunch without feeling guilty. Well, they do provide such good buffets at the best ones and it would be a waste not to at least put something on one's plate. A lettuce leaf and a spoon of *tabbouleh* is a very elegant arrangement and sends just the right message of sympathy to those who notice such things even in times of grief. And of course, one must not forget that eating does make one feel better. The look? Well, Marlene's standard uniform is scraped-back hair, dress by *Alia*, *Prada* sunglasses and a well-clutched Kleenex. She has a veil for Muslim funerals, something she picked up in Rome that really hits the spot.

-MK

Lebanese Colonel

A long and loyal if not particularly illustrious career was winding down towards retirement when Souhail thought his moment of glory had finally arrived. Almost by accident - it was early on a Sunday morning - he was the first senior officer on the scene at the suspected murder of a foreigner. He carefully began drawing up a list of suspects and motives to impress the senior security personnel who would undoubtedly become involved. However, after several other agencies probed the scene of the death and the victim's background, it (sadly for Souhail) emerged that the foreigner had not been pushed over a 40-foot cliff but had lost his footing and fallen. A last chance at investigative glory had been snatched away from Souhail. Since reassigned to a quiet backwater, he surveys his new kingdom: a crumbling building with dark and dirty windows, an interior paint job reminiscent of a 1950s London lavatory and an office whose only virtue was that it is his. The paperwork on his battered, grey metal desk is less a mountain than a hillock, but Souhail goes through the sparse files daily, making meticulous notes and marking his initials. Not that anyone is ever going to use or even open most of them. Reports of stolen property fall into two categories: the ones which are filed by people who don't matter (and therefore cannot expect much attention), and those filed by people whose status demands the might of the law be seen swinging into action. Even if the result in both cases is roughly equal. But there aren't many people of note in Souhail's new district, and his comments on the files are rarely read. If only that foolish foreigner had made a few interesting enemies instead of taking a drink too many, life for Souhail could be so different.

-PG

Newspaper Seller

Abdullah's father and grandfather also sold papers, so it was natural that he follow in their footsteps. Who would do this voluntarily? He stands at the junction of Tabaris and Avenue Charles Malek and performs what he sees as a vital service. Of course he has his regular clients, and he even plays a game with himself when someone pulls up, guessing what language publication they will ask for. Happy moments apart, the job does have its dark side. He has nearly been killed a dozen times and ended up in the hospital on three occasions - once when a minister's convoy ploughed into the back of Mrs. Frangieh who was buying her monthly copy of *Fantastique*. They all got out shouting and screaming and firing pistols in the air. They thought Abdullah had been part of an elaborate ambush. The minister, who was sitting with his secretary, was thrown through the windscreen and landed on him. The minister was ok, but Abdullah broke his back. He was in all the papers and, after being interrogated by general security and cleared of being a ruthless terrorist, he was hailed as a hero for saving the minister's life. Can you imagine it, the one day he was in the paper, and he was in the hospital! He reasoned that the next time he would make it into the press would be when he died, so he enjoyed it while he could. Mrs. Frangieh sent flowers and *baklawa* and the minister paid the bills. The doctors told him about lead poisoning in his lungs, but we all have to go sometime.

-MK

Expat Consultant

Beirut gave Don every opportunity he needed to wipe out the failures of the past. His status was assured by the title of "Communications Consultant" and a salary five times the size of Lebanese younger, brighter and better. Throw in the Antelias flat, car and driver and Mr. Donald, as he came to be known, began to believe his own myths. Made redundant after 27 years in telecoms, Don knew his payoff wouldn't sustain his wife's acquired tastes. His last employer's parting favour had been to nominate him for a European-funded, three-year consultancy in Lebanon. In a stroke of luck, it concerned an aspect of communications in which he could make people believe he knew what he was talking about. Join local associations, especially any that have connections to a charity, Don had been advised. So he signed up for the joint Lebanese Business Association and each month, armed with the pick of a couple of pages from *Acceptable Jokes to Tell at Dinner Parties*, he strode out to become a star of the outfit. But for the bad teeth and even worse breath, he might even have succeeded. As it was, few talked to him from less than several feet away, no matter how good the jokes. Gatherings at the expat pub on half-price Fridays seemed more socially successful. Yet if people were (literally) less standoffish than at the business association meetings, it was maybe because they shared his lack of attention to personal hygiene. In any case, *Naughty Tales to Tell the Lads* seemed to draw more laughs than its tamer companion volume. In regulation consultant suit, white shirt and striped tie, Don even did well with the young Lebanese women in search of a foreign chequebook... until they discovered his reputation for a foul mouth wasn't based only on the *Naughty Lads* joke book.

-PG

97

World Cup Supporter

In '98, Ali supported Brazil (he was not going to make the same mistake he made in '94 by supporting Italy, even though he drove a *Fiat*), but then France came along and ruined it. So in 2002, he initially put his money on France (he didn't drive a Renault, but he was sure they would win). After France's early exit, it was very difficult to put up his Brazil flag without the neighbors noticing, but it was worth it. He should never have deviated in the first place, especially as his grandfather went to Sao Paulo at the turn of the century and his father was born there (ok, he had to flee the country after being wanted for cattle theft and murder). His brother Hussein supports Germany because he has long admired the German sense of order and engineering (yes, you guessed it, he drives a 1974 Mercedes 200 which has done 2 million kilometres) while Ali's son, Malik, is now old enough to make his own choices and supports England. His wife has supported Italy since 1994 when Baggio had a ponytail. It annoys him how women always comment about the handsome ones when it has nothing to do with football. Anyway, the French players are all Arabs and Africans. What type of team is that? Like last time, he will make a bit of money on the side and produce his own flags. His cousin has a factory in Dekwayne. But he must be careful. Brazil had better pull through this time.

-MK

City Centre Waiter

At first Mahmoud thought he would die of embarrassment at the uniform. I mean, just look at it. White trousers and shirt, black shoes, a red, yellow and blue striped blazer, all topped off with a ribboned straw hat. He looked like a refugee from some minor US college rowing club. But he needed money to pay off his debts after the excesses of the last university semester, and waiting tables downtown at *Chez Charles* seemed like a good idea at the time. The pay was ridiculously low, the hours long and the expressions he was ordered to use with the customers made him cringe. Who in his right mind would say, "Hello, my name's Mahmoud. I'll be your waiter this evening, and I'm here to make your meal a memorable experience"? But that was the 'California style' the owner wanted. So that's what he said. And Mahmoud soon discovered the formula brought in healthy tips from the summer crowds. The obligatory return to a table five minutes after serving the food (in which presentation seemed to be valued over substance, rather like the uniform) with a cheery, "Is everything to your liking, sir?" only heightened the impression of care and attentiveness. And as the money rolled in, Mahmoud got to know the other staff. Students like himself, they were certainly more interesting than the clientele. Their snatched conversations between waiting on customers became longer. The greeting formula became faster and even more devoid of sincerity than it was at the beginning. Mahmoud and his co-worker friends became experts at avoiding the customers' eyes and even their waving hands. After all, they'd gotten their welcome and had their meals served, what more did they expect? Anything extra was interrupting a serious student conversation about the destiny of the country. And Charles was left wondering why the approach worked in 'Frisco but not here.

-PG

Mountain Arak Producer

Elias has been making *arak* for 50 years. He was taught by his father and learned to perfect the technique just before that fateful day when the *Karkeh* exploded in the cellar, atomising Abou Elias and his uncle. Um Elias suggested that it would be safer to buy the commercial brands, now that he was the family's sole income provider, but he gave her a lecture about commercial brands being stuffed with chemicals. She responded that it was surely better to be stuffed with chemicals than to have the walls of her qabbu still stuffed with the remains of her husband. Elias argued that God wanted them that day and nothing would bring them back. To honor their memory, he would make the purest *arak*. Ethanol? What is Ethanol? One of his earliest memories was watching his grandfather drink *arak* with a breakfast of *kafta awarma* and raw liver. "Surely it's not healthy," he asked his *jiddu*. Abou Najeeb, who was known as a bit of a scoundrel - or *abaday* as Elias prefers to remember him - replied: *"la jiddu, hayda dawa!"* It's medicine. It was an adage he took to heart, especially when his best friend Roukoz asked for a bottle a day after a triple bypass. "He told me the doctor had said it was ok," recalls Elias. "This proved that Abou Najeeb, *Allah yirhamu*, was right when he said it was medicine." Unfortunately, Roukoz died the next day. "Doctors!" Elias shakes his head. "What do they know? Donkeys! All of them."

-MK

Traffic Queue Jumper

Nabil's logic was flawless. At least to him. He was a better driver than everyone else. He had a better car than most - a 4-liter V8 convertible with a flawless exterior. Of course it didn't have a scratch on it. As a child, he had practiced avoiding all the other bumper cars at fairgrounds; now he was putting that experience to good use. Nabil's first rule of the road was that any empty space in the traffic ahead belonged to him. It didn't matter if it was on the left and he wanted to turn right (or vice versa). It was his, and any method of getting from here to the opening 20 metres ahead was fair game. A particular favorite was using the extra road width offered by storefront parking lots like those on the coastal highway through Zalka. Oh, those foolish *Aziz* shoppers who thought they were safe loading the trunks of their cars when Nabil was in a hurry! Spotting a gap and using the instant power of his motor to fill it worked as a strategy on the highway, but for two-way roads, it was a different matter altogether. At the least sign of traffic going in his direction, Nabil switched to driving on the left hand side of the road, defying everyone and anyone to get out of the way. Headlights blazing at all times of the day, he would intimidate oncoming drivers off onto the sidewalks with a technique that involved being not slightly, but completely on the wrong side of the road. But it was Nabil's system for avoiding line-ups at open air parking lots that was his masterpiece: enter backwards at great speed through the exit lane and steal one of few spots available while lesser mortals are still changing gear.

-PG

Supermarket Man

Michel knows exactly what he wants. He walks into the supermarket like a god - shirt slashed open showing a brace of gold chains nestled on a rug of chest hair and smoking a cigar (it helps him think) and grabs one of the boys to push the trolley. Why his wife doesn't think of that, he will never know. And so the shopping process begins. He will not be taken for a fool. Just because his wife normally does the shopping, it doesn't mean he can't, and so he uses these opportunities to show her just how superior he is in every way. If she were to leave him - a threat that has become hollow over the years - he *would* cope. His preferred section for demonstrating his retail savvy is the cold meats counter. He doesn't queue. Why should he? He is his mother's son, after all. He sees the other customers accept their ham from an "opened" pack. *Hameer!* How long do they think it has been there? Michel will always demand, blowing cigar smoke over the counter, that the man open a new one. He then tastes the meat and approves the thickness of the slice. Not that he cares. It's just that he wants them to know who's boss - in case they didn't already - and if he has to take a phone call, then let them wait. That's how Michel sees life. Always make sure you get one over on the little guy, because all the little guys in the world are out to get you. Well, that's what his late father told him anyway.

-MK

Nosy Neighbour

If she had ever been allowed a career of her own, Sabine would have made an ace (if low-level) spy. Never permitted to leave her home unaccompanied while growing up, she eventually exchanged the domestic imprisonment she had known as a youngster for the incarceration imposed by a husband who knew exactly where a wife's place was. (And mixing with the bad influences to be found away from their home in Badaro wasn't it.) So she began to borrow a taste of what she was missing by sneaking a peep through the windows at other people's lives. A mother proudly parading her newborn. Lovers stealing a kiss when they thought no one was around. Even a fight between a customer and a street vendor. Armed with the binoculars she had requested on the pretext of observing wildlife at their mountain house, Sabine became an expert on the neighbourhood's habits - and especially those of the people in her building. She could watch strangers enter and know exactly which floor they were visiting by the length of time the elevator motor ran. (The jeweller's wife on the 4th floor had the same visitor every Monday, Wednesday and Friday at exactly 3pm.) Sabine had arranged her curtains so that from one window or another she could see all that happened in front of the building. No one entered unseen. Awaiting the post-midnight return of her own spouse, she began to notice he was not the only one to keep late hours. She even developed Sabine-speak. Thus to a neighbour, "Your Jean is working very hard these days," meant, "I heard him coming home after a night in the pub." And if only she could have revealed to people across the road the evidence gathered through her bird-watching binoculars.

-PG

Sunday Party Activist

Boudi and his friends like nothing better on a Sunday than to drive around the neighbourhood waving banners adorned with pictures of the "Engineer." Boudi is aware that the Engineer is a politician - no, a national saviour - and that his father worships him. The fact that his best mate Rabih also likes him is enough. The Engineer must be a good guy because on the Engineer's birthday (or was it the anniversary of someone dying? He can't remember), he was paid to drive around waving a flag emblazoned with an exclamation mark, the Engineer's logo. Boudi also feels it's important to look the part: he wears cargo pants, "Ranger" boots and a t-shirt which hugs so much it shows his belly, but who cares? It's what the Engineer's bodyguards wear and heck, given the job market, that wouldn't be a bad option. The Engineer has told him they are all family, so they all have to stick together. Sunday driving is sticking together. It has its own hierarchy. Fadi drives the car while Boudi sits in the front with the big flag. His younger brother Kameel stands out of the sunroof while two of Kameel's friends just sit in the back, wearing moronic grins and tapping cigarette lighters on their knees as the speakers blare out Najwa Karam. When they bore of driving up and down the same strip of highway 50 times, they try to distract bike riders doing wheelies. His father, although a disciple of the Engineer, despairs of him and wishes he would go back to Miami College in Zouk, where he was studying for a diploma in inventory control. It wasn't like this in his day. Kids had respect.

-MK

Printing: **dots**